letters to Gypsy

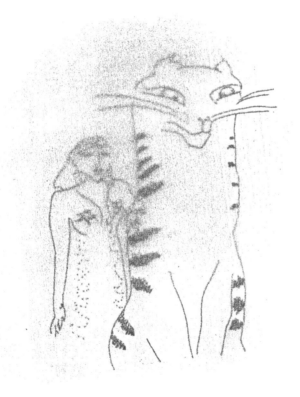

Other titles by

George Mackay Brown

include:

Poems
Fishermen with Ploughs
Loaves and Fishes
The Year of the Whale
Winterfold
Voyages

Short Stories
A Calendar of Love
A Time to Keep
Hawkfall
The Sun's Net
Andrina
The Golden Bird
The Masked Fisherman

Plays
A Spell for Green Corn
The Loom of Light
A Celebration for Magnus
Three Plays

Novels
Greenvoe
Magnus
Time in a Red Coat

Non-Fiction
Portrait of Orkney

For Children
The Two Fiddlers
Pictures in The Cave
Six Lives of Fankle the Cat

Essays
An Orkney Tapestry
Letters from Hamnavoe
Under Brinkie's Brae

Folio/ Special books
The Bestiary (The Parragon Press)
Stone (K.D.Duval)
St Magnus Poems (E. Gore-Langton)

Letters to GYPSY

George Mackay Brown

pictures by Simon Fraser

BALNAIN BOOKS

Printed and bound in Britain by Billings and Sons Ltd.,
Worcester.
Colour printed by Wood Westworth.

Published in 1990
by Balnain Books,
Druim House, Lochloy Road,
Nairn IV12 5LF.
Scotland

British Library Cataloguing in Publication Data:
Brown, George Mackay 1921-
      Letters to Gypsy.
      I. Title
      823.914 [F]

ISBN 1-872557-02-3

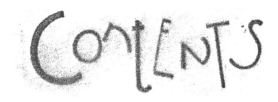

CONTENTS

for

Nora Kennedy

Birsay, and afterwards lived for a brief time in a caravan nearby, with Tam and Gunnie and four MacPhail boys.

Then Nora Kennedy adopted her, as a tiny kitten, to live in a cottage in South Ronaldsay called Dyke-end, where she stalked cows.

It was a great change for Gypsy to come and live in Stromness, that town of stone and sea in the west. She lived in a house in Dundas Street, on a stone, sea-washed pier. Often, as will be seen, she dreams of ancestral palaces in Egypt and Babylon.

Whenever she allowed Nora to go south, to Edinburgh or Italy or Beauly, she sometimes consented to live for a few days or weeks in the house of a writer in Stromness, at Mayburn Court. She wasn't too enamoured of the council house at Mayburn Court, without greenery or pier. Still, she and the writer got on reasonably well; though occasionally he complained about this female tyrant who broke his bachelor tranquillity, demanding food, taking over the rocking chair.

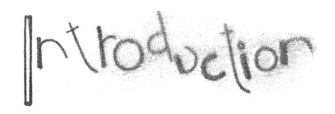

Introduction

So that non-Orcadian readers won't be confused, there ought to be a note about Gypsy's various residencies in Orkney.

She was born in the Mill of Boardhouse in

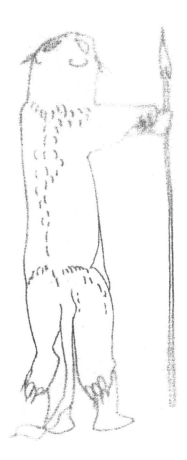

Whenever Gypsy went back home, the writer missed her so much that in the end he decided he must write her a weekly letter.

Gypsy's letters to the writer — if they exist at all — must be inscribed on such light ethereal insubstantial tissue-of-moonbeam that even the glance of an eye might destroy them. It is possible that they are stored in a "crystal cave deep in the diamond of the day" along with the other treasures of Merlin the enchanter.

After years in Dundas Street, Gypsy moved to a cottage in Deerness, twenty miles away and more, called Noltland, and there she quickly made herself known to the local fauna: cows and birds, mice and rabbits and voles.

As I write this, she is a dignified elderly plump cat, and she reminds me a bit of Queen Victoria in the seventies and eighties of the last century. But she retains the eternal spirit of playfulness, and still the springs of poetry never fail in her.

A few years ago, I wrote a short essay about Gypsy for "The Scotsman", that might throw some light on our special relationship:

In about half an hour, Gypsy the cat will be here.

For more than a fortnight I have gone down to a cold empty house on a pier to feed Gypsy out of a tin. The plastic litter basin has to be seen to. The saucer of water too (for she doesn't like milk, it seems.)

Gypsy's mistress is in Edinburgh. I have been

appointed her keeper.

If everybody in the world greeted me the way Gypsy does, as soon as she hears the key in the lock! She forgives everything; the cold, the loneliness, the desolation. She can hardly wait to nestle and burrow her head in my coat. She brims with lyrics of pure joy.

Oh, let me feel the hardness of your knuckles on my skull! I have a terrible itch at the throat — scratch it — and between the ears also! And again...

And I keep uttering bits of nonsense, like "Gypsums-mypsums..." "Who's the loveliest pussy in all the world?"... "A night and a day — was she sad then?"

This little snatch of opera goes on for quite a time before there is any thought of food.

But, of course, after those preliminaries, the serious business of food is to be considered.

The tin of rabbit, or fish, or beef, or heart, is in the closed cupboard. Take one step in that direction, and Gypsy remembers that she's hungry — not a bite for 24 hours. She can hardly wait

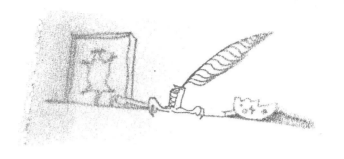

for me to get the food on to the plate.

Never mind chopping it up with the spoon... Just leave me for a while... There has never in this world been such hunger...

She sets about her single course with a will. Fiercely and delicately she eats, and contrives somehow to sing at the same time. Human beings can't manage that — when you think about it, there has hardly been a decent poem about food — except perhaps for that tumult of dainties in *The Eve of St Agnes.* There may be a banquet in Milton's *Comus* too, a shadow in the mind from days in the class-room. (But poets, even so, rarely write and eat simultaneously.)

Gypsy knows quite well I'll soon be leaving her, and she'll be alone and wretched again for 24 hours.

None of that... Wait a bit... I have a few more things to say to you, two or three items.

So, knowing that the key is in my hand, she leaves her meal half-eaten, and we have another ten-minute dialogue. Her eyes blaze like diamonds in the gray air of the house. She is well, she's in good condition; her black coat is thick and glossy.

It can't last for too long. I have messages to get in the shops — including cat food — and words to write before nightfall. Ashamed of my cruelty, I leave her smartly, closing the door before she can follow.

Last Thursday was a beautiful afternoon, and so I let Gypsy out for a stroll. She loves to promenade about the piers and the narrow chasms between tall sea-fronting houses. When the tide is far out, she goes sure-footed among the slippery seaweed. She might encounter a gull — they consider each other for a while, till the gull spreads leisured wings seawards. Occasionally she has dragged a water-rat right up to the yard of the house, as if to say,

How's this for a piece of good hunting?

The November sun last Thursday softened my heart. Gypsy slipped through the door like a black shadow, silent as a fish through a breached net. Here and there she went, her eyes full of wonder. "Make the most of the next half-hour,"

I said, "for then it's back to the prison-house with you"...

I walked down the big pier of Hamnavoe and looked at the berthed silent fishing boats. There's an eagerness and mellowness in an early November afternoon that makes breathing a sensuous delight.

When I got back to Gypsy's pier, Gypsy wasn't there. She's no fool, Gypsy. I swear that cat is wittier than many a human being. Among the little labyrinth of paths and closes I went, calling, "Gypsy . . . Gypsy . . . Gypsy" Not a "meouw", not a little footfall anywhere. Gypsy was taking the afternoon off.

Thank you. Go away. I am in one of my secret places. Come back at suppertime. I am quite happy...

I could have kicked her − but not too hard − for her truancy and delinquency and selfishness.

The truth is, I don't like going out on a dark cold night in late autumn. I want to sit in the rocking chair with a book or a TV programme.

Would I leave Gypsy out all night? She has

been out all night before, in summer, and taken no harm. But supposing a storm blew up after midnight, a frenzy of wind and rain and spindrift? Supposing I went down the next afternoon, and found a stark little black corpse on the the pier, braided with seaweed?

I dragged on shoes and coat, and trekked through the winding street. And down the steps. And there she was, waiting, an exquisite piece of blackness in the gloom. In she went. We serenaded each other, with purrs and nonsense, for five minutes or so.

This has gone on for more than a fortnight. Gypsy's owner was due back at the end of last week. She phoned from Edinburgh — appointments with a dentist — she wouldn't be home for two more weeks.

I'm expecting my niece Judith any minute now with the black bundle in her arms. Judith has a way with animals. If I tried to carry Gypsy along the street, she would scratch and coil her way out of my keeping before I had gone twenty paces.

Everything will be all right. Gypsy has stayed with me before, more than once. She tolerates my house, but only just. This corner of Hamna-voe is swarming with cats, and Gypsy is half afraid of them. I think an old pugnacious tomcat gave her a beating-up one summer day; since then she is apprehensive.

No, thank you, I won't go out. I know the sun is shining, but I'd rather be indoors. If you don't mind.

The only concession she will make to the great outside is to sit inside the window and look down at the comings and goings on the street with her great brilliant eyes.

The rocking-chair, when she stays here, is no longer mine. I have to make do, as best I can, curled up in the couch with my book, or watching the gray shadows on the TV screen.

I think, when she's living here, she misses the sea and the gulls. On summer afternoons at home she sits on the yard wall, right on the corner, woven about with sea sounds and sea images.

"Everything is ready, Gypsy. This is not such a nice place, I know, as your home ground. But you won't be so lonely. We won't have little operatic duets of such intensity; but two or three times a day, besides food and sleep, we will murmur poems to one another..."

· · · · · · · · · ·

By Gypsy's gracious permission these letters are now published...

G.M.B.

Stromness

Dear Gyps,

Thank you for your lovely letters.

I never knew such a clever cat at writing letters, your spelling, punctuation and grammar
are all impeccable.

I think, Gypsy, you should write your autobio-
graphy and have it ready (typewritten by Nan
Butcher) for April.

How about that?

And how would it begin?

*"I was born in a caravan in Birsay in the year
1976. I had brothers and sisters, the most famous
of whom was a brother called Fankle. Fankle had
an exciting but brief life. He was cut down mys-
teriously in the flower of his youth, found dead in
a summer-tide garden, with butterflies weaving
slow, elegiac dances around him, and all the
flowers with dew of grief in them. That death has
never been satisfactorily explained. I may yet call
in Miss Marple or Maigret — though I think
Sherlock Holmes (who, alas, is no longer with us)*

AUTOBIOGRAPHER

would certainly have got to the bottom of it.

"My mother was called Tiny.

"My father must have been a fine tom-cat, a gay philanderer with an air of poetry and romance about him. I wish I knew more about him, the hero.

"Now, when I was quite small we moved to the vicinity of a hill-top farm in Stromness, and there one day as I was playing with my brothers and sisters..."

You get the hang of it, Gypsy? It will be serialised in the *News of the World*, perhaps.

NEXT WEEK

– GYPSY'S FIRST LOVE AFFAIR –

READ ALL ABOUT IT!...

It'll be a knock-out!

INTO HiSTORY for PEDIGREE

CONTRACTUAL

Dear Gyps,

Coming to me, are you, Gyps?
Coming for a week or so?
Is that so?
Is that a fact?
Well…
Well well well –
Let's get certain things clear, Gyps.

aGREEMENT

You are to have a walk
Every morning, a walk
For the good of your health,
A delicate ladylike walk
Along the balcony.
Is that clear?
Now, about sitting and sleeping.
G has the rocking chair – OK? –
Whenever he wants to read.
The rest of the time , it's yours.
Now, about meal times.

I want no howls of hunger,
Desperate wails of starvation
Such as would melt a stone heart
Whenever
You see me going into the kitchen.
Three **strict** mealtimes a day.
Understand?
And if you sit on the windowsill
Don't
Knock over the jar of daffodils.
And if you're heartbroken
Or have any complaints whatever
Nora's phone-number's in the book,
Also
Society for Prevention of Cruelty to Cats.
(Prompt payment required for all phone-calls.)
The door to your private toilet
Will always be open,
But be sure you flush the loo.
OK Gypsy?..

OK
Be seein' you,

aBANDONED

Dear Gyps,

There's your guardian, Nora, off on the 'Ola' this morning, leaving you in the prison of Mayburn – and not a bite to eat, if the prison warden hadn't gone first thing down to the peedie shop for a tin of Whiskas beef.

Not one grain of cat litter did she leave.
"Oh," cries Gyp, "*what'll I do for my toilet?*"
That will be seen to.

There, she's been sleeping all morning in the straw chair while GMB sees to his poems and letters.

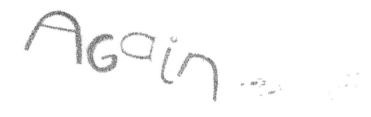

Oh, how I miss my pier.
No more can I speak to gulls.
Nora has left me again! –
Gone to talk to a man
Called Napoleon, in Elba,
Gone to talk to somebody called Dante
And Fra Filipo Lippi (what names!)
In Tuscany.
Tonight I'll be so lonely
When G goes to Garth for supper.
What a fright I get, always,
When the telephone rings,
When some tourist knocks at the door.
Still, I can watch
The birds, insects, and fish on TV.
(Nora doesn't have that.)
And I have three rooms I can sleep in.

That's what you sang in the straw chair all morning: while poor G grunted and groaned over his
letters and poems.

Dear Gyps,

So you want me to trace your ancestry, do you?
Away far back to Assyria and Babylon.

Let me tell you, Gypsy, men and cats who dig
into their ancestry sometimes bring some dread-
ful things to light.

However, if you're willing to take the risk...

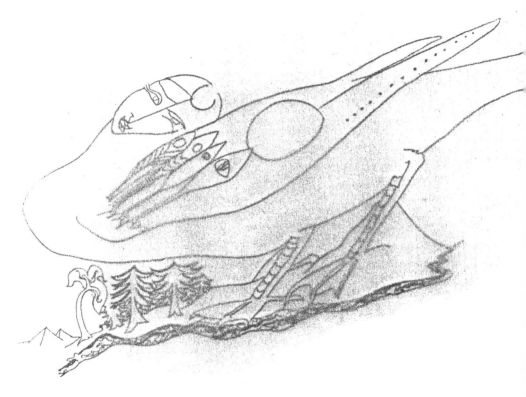

for Pedigree

I have engaged a formidable team of researchers and secretaries to begin operations. This will have to be in London, in a concrete and steel office block near the British Museum. A woman will be employed to make endless cups of coffee. An office boy, with ink-splotches on his shirt collar (possibly a glue-sniffer) will empty the waste-paper baskets. There will be 20 telephones, 3 fax machines. An eminent professor of Oriental Studies will be the overall boss.

I expect I'll have to fly down once a month to see how the work is going.

The planning committee thinks that the project might take a year. (That means, in my experience, nearer 2 years.)

The amount of work involved will, of course, be colossal.

All to find out how such a pussycat as you, Gyps, happened to open kittenish innocent eyes in the barbarous Orkneys in the late 1970's.

Hold on to your seat-belt. It might be a rough ride. Or it might be an incursion into a feline paradise.

Many thousands of books, papyrus documents and stone tablets will have to be consulted…

Return of the Rats

Dear Gyps

You'll never believe this, but 2 days ago I had visitors – such shy bashful creatures that they wouldn't even show themselves or say,

"How d'you do – how about a piece of cheese or a slice of bacon with a good fringe of fat on it? – here we are for the winter..."

No, but I heard them merrily playing between the walls, running hither and thither and kicking up their heels, occasionally chewing a brick or a joist; then all was silent again – I could imagine them having a whispered conference on what to do next.

Well, I guess a clever cat like you knows by now who my bashful uninvited guests are: RATS.

If they think they're coming here for the winter, Gypsy, to be my little bright-eyed friends and eat crumbs and apple-cores from my fingers, and warm their whiskers and tails at my fire, they're making a big mistake...

I know them; they'll go and leave me some

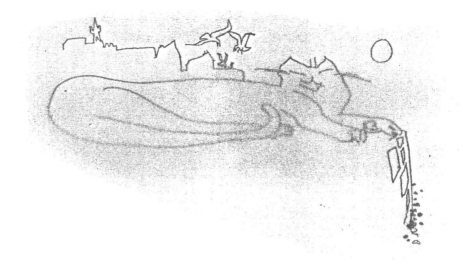

charming "thank-you" gift like bubonic plague. So, I think I'll have to look for some smart ruthless-looking, no-nonsense cat in one of the pierside houses, one from a long rat-knowledgeable pedigree, and instal him (or her) as my guardian.

How he (or she) would listen at every conceivable crack and hole, and catch the least rat-whisper, and say to himself or herself:

"Come, little guests, George has appointed me his receptionist-in-chief – I will attend to you with utmost despatch!..."

Isn't that a good idea?

Or would you be upset at the thought of such an invigilator in this house?

Star of Egypt

Dear Gyps,

I hear there were lightning flashes last night, and rattling hail.

I hope you weren't frightened, all alone in Dundas St... Of course I know that brave cats like Gypsy aren't afraid of volcano, flood, earthquake, hurricane.

Still, it can't be easy for *felix domesticus* who lived for hundreds of years under the hot suns of Egypt, and took fish out of the Nile with nimble paws.

I wonder how your ancestors came to Orkney, Gyps?

Well, pin your ears back and listen. Your very remote ancestress was Queen Cleopatra's favourite cat... After that queen had put the asp to her bosom, that cat got into a little boat and sailed to Sicily. Her great-granddaughter got scared of the Mafia and their knives, so the boat was launched again and the little cat family sailed through the Pillars of Hercules until they came to Ireland. They thought they would get peace there, among the green hills, but there was nothing but trouble with the I.R.A. and the Orangemen.

So they rowed across to Argyll. Then your mother and great-uncle (Tiny and Spot) emigrated to Orkney, in Tam and Gunnie's van. And there, in a caravan in Birsay, you first saw the light, Gypsy, little star of Egypt.

William & the New

Dear Gyps,

Do you know who's coming today?
– Brian Murray.

He'll be coming – Eliza too – off the 'Ola' at 2 o'clock.

Oh, fancy coming to a cold house in mid-winter; no food in the cupboard, no fire blinking in the grate, no chairs even. They'll have, once more, to get the loan of G's 2 green bedroom chairs to sit on.

But even so, Brian Murray will be laughing to himself with joy, just to be in Orkney.

I think there should have been a nice cat to

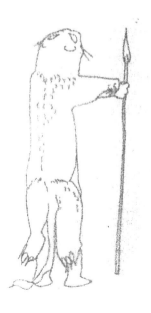

Year Crowds

greet him on the doorstep – such as one or two cats I've known in my time.

Then Brian and Eliza would have felt really at home.

Two nights ago, William Bevan sat on my knee for twenty minutes or so. What's that – you don't know such a creature as William Bevan... William Bevan is your *son*, Gypsy, a very handsome cat indeed, and very like his mother, only longer and thinner. Well, William sang me a New Year song. More and more people came into Hopedale, troops of them, and at last William said,

> "That's enough for me... What do they think this place is, a fairground?.. Tell you the truth, I get claustrophobia among such a dense throng of humanity"...

He slipped off my knee like a shadow, and possibly became one with the night, because William goes out every night and he likes a crowd of stars more than a crowd of beer-swelling revellers.

A happy New Year, Gyps.

Flame of Life

Dear Gyps,

I heard the strangest true story about you the other day.

You almost never got beyond your dewy-and-midnight kittenhood.

Did you know, for instance, that you were born in the famous Mill of Boardhouse in Birsay?

Well, you were. Tiny MacPhail — your mother — chose the loft there for you and your four brothers and sisters to be born.

And nobody knew but Tiny. Tiny was keeping it for a surprise.

However, it was Tiny who got a surprise when she was suddenly bundled into a van and driven down to live in a caravan near Stromness.

"What's wrong with Tiny?" thought Gunnie after the second or third day, "Tiny's taking a long while to settle down. Tiny seems to be very anxious and afraid..."

Then it was obvious: Tiny had been snatched away untimely from her secret new-born "kettlings"! So back the van rattled to Birsay, with Tiny in it, and no sooner was the door open than Tiny jumped out and ran to the mill and up the stairs like a black pitchball from a volcano, and there in a cosy corner were 5 tiny, black, blind kittens that hadn't seen or tasted or smelt nourishment for three whole days.

Well, Gypsy, I must say you've made up for that long fast, ever since. Never was there a greedier kitten. Nobody, even today, could call you Twiggy Kennedy... Well, it suits you. One of your fellow fasters was your brother, the famous Fankle.

Long-Time no

Dear Gyps,

Such a long time since we had a little talk!

I have been down to your house 3 or 4 times, and I only saw you once through the glass, darkly.

All doors were locked!

Gyps, I think Nora is keeping you a prisoner in that house, like Mary Queen of Scots in Fotheringay Castle. I could dig a tunnel under the house and rescue you that way. Or perhaps you are like Richard Coeur de Lion imprisoned on his way back from the Crusades. So, some day, I might come and sing troubadour songs under your barred window. Then you will know that help is on the way.

I bet you're glad it's a lovely day, and all the snow is in Kirkwall and here the day is an opal, an emerald and a crystal.

Sometimes the rocking chair says, "Whatever's become of Gypsy?"

Sometimes the window sill whispers, "I miss that nice black- silky pussy sitting on me, looking out."

And the stair says, "I'm tired of that old George clumping up and down – there was a beautiful creature here, she flowed up and down as light as a breeze or a butterfly."

Dear Gyps,

What's that, you want to know your ancestry?

Do you think for one moment I have the time or the resources to go through the books of feline geneologies of Babylon and Egypt?

Well, I don't.

But I have an invisible friend, the Muse, who tells me a thing or two.

So pin your ears back. Hearken.

On the fifth day from the very beginning, the Creator made the animals, all of them, fleas, kangaroos, sharks, eagles, elephants, snakes, voles. So he thought,

"That's a good day's work. Tomorrow: Man, and *he's* going to be a problem, I can foresee that"...

The Life-Force (as some agnostics and rationalists call him) was just going to have a lie-down, when an angel sang out,

Oh, Ancient-of-Days, just look at that bit of jungle in Africa set alight by a lightning stroke! Isn't it magnificent, the way it moves and rages

and roams here and there!
And the Creator looked and said,
    Let there be an animal like that called **CAT.**

So that was the first cat, but if you think it was a bit like you, Gypsy, you're much mistaken.

It was more like a lion or a tiger: the original pristine cat.

And oh! he was magnificent.

Such a marvellous creature strolled over to join the congregation of the animals: "Tyger Tyger burning bright/ In the forests of the night"... as a later poet was to call him.

Out of that glory of five came at last all cats,

even the little cats that sit beside fires in houses and purr and cry,
"Milk, give me a saucer of milk, before I sleep, at once, you slow-coach."

Opposite: Taming the First Cat

Cat-Foods

Dear Gyps,

There was once a black cat and advertising people thought they would test all kinds of catfood on this cat to see which catfood she liked best.

"Bits of cheese?"...*Take it away.*

"Cold meat from the butcher?"... *How dare you bring that stuff and set it in front of me!*

"Kattomeat? Kit-E-Kat? Whiskas?"... *They're all quite good. But what I should really be getting – a cat of my quality and pedigree – is smoked salmon and caviar. I have aristocratic tastes.*

Along came Nora with some liver to fry for her supper. Then this snobbish gourmet of a black cat went slightly crazy –

Liver! liver! liver! she cried. *I long for nothing but liver. My life is consumed with lust for liver!... I shall die if I don't get a saucer-ful of chopped liver, at once...*

Then the advertising consultants and the TV crew packed their equipment and sailed off on the 'Ola'.

The last thing they heard was Gypsy singing at the pier wall:

Liver!
You are the loveliest food ever.
My stomach gives a shiver,
A flutter and a quiver,
Whenever I think of that food,
So surpassingly good.
As sure as I sit on this pier
Even caviar
Would taste awful
Compared to liver, that glorious offal.
Now that I've supped deep,
I think I might curl up and go to sleep

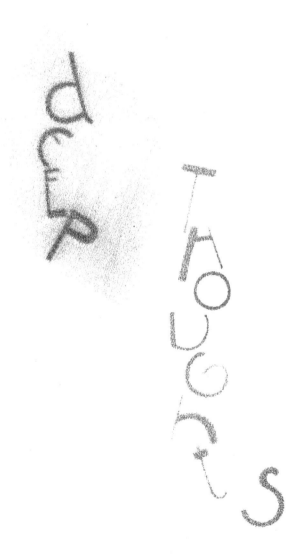

deep THOUGHTS

Dear Gyps,

I hope you are enjoying the sun, even though the north wind is cold if you linger at the edge of the pier.

I see you have a lovely show of dandelions this year, at Dundas Street.

But where – oh where – is the table I used to sit at in the yard, and sometimes drink Nora's delicious coffee? Where is the fine chair with the arms where I used to lounge and watch the harbour, the fishing boats and the gulls? I can see it is going to be a very austere summer in your yard, Gypsy.

So please go along to the carpenter and order a strong table, capable of enduring all weathers, and a comfortable chair for me to sit and write poems. At the same time, he could build you a little octagonal garden house where you could indulge in cultural activities – books and painting watercolours – with a divan suitable for artistic lady cats to lie down on.

Chair

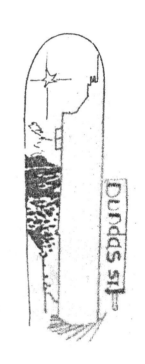

You'd better see to that quite soon, Gypsy, before the summer visitors come.

sillock-Taster

Dear Gyps,

What on earth are cats coming to?

Once, when the boys of Hamnavoe fished for sillocks off the piers, there was sure to be a cat or two lingering there, waiting to relish those bits of flashing silver-gray newly out of the harbour.

Oh, how delicately they ate them, right down to the bone, except maybe the tail and fins.

There was nothing on earth the Stromness cats liked so much as fresh sillocks. Except maybe *'lights'* from the butcher, and bits of liver.

You won't believe this, but the other day a boy came with sillocks to a certain cat, and the cat looked at them and – she didn't know what to do with them.

"What's this lot?" she said. *"What am I supposed to do with them ? EAT THEM! Nothing doing. What do they take me for? My dinner comes out of tins – I won't eat anything that doesn't come out of a tin... Take those slimy things away, at once..."*

Did you ever hear of such a stupid cat?

However, I believe that after a time she rather began to enjoy the sea-smells coming off them. After another while, she had an experimental bite or two... At last a little feast.

Some cats are strange, aren't they, Gyps?

Dear Gyps,

You must have heard about Billie Ramsey the Faravel cat.

Well, Billie was lonely when Joanna her mother was in Aberdeen last weekend.

Billie has a cat door so she can take the fresh air whenever she wants to, then return to sleep on the quilt. A neighbour feeds her.

Last Sunday – remember? – had only a few cold splashes of sun. I saw Billie at her front door, hoping (like me) that the sun would come out warm and bright. "Hello Billie," I called from the steps. Billie looked through me as though I was made of glass. If she did meaow, it would have been,

> "*Get on your way, my man – you're standing between me and whatever sun there is*"...

Well, yesterday afternoon Joanna returned, and Billie saw her from the neighbour's garden and came galloping softly to meet her. Oh, she was pleased! I'm sure she purred and sang and purred for hours, between eating a 'welcome home' meal and opening her present from Aberdeen.

"She's back for keeps" said Billie. *"Good."*

But Joanna had to go out later that evening and visit friends.

And when Billie saw that she was making preparations to quit the house once more, she was very angry. Do you know what she did? – she bit Joanna's finger, hard.

"There – take that! – as a sign of my disapproval".

Still, in Billie's heart of hearts, she's delighted. By the way, Billie had left little tufts of her fur all over the carpet.

"Look how clever I am, decorating the living-room for you while you've been away"…

Be nice to the little new blackbirds, Gypsy.

Dear Gyps,

What a place this is, the sun and the fog are forever fighting with each other. Now one wins, now the other.

They say cats love the fog. Well, a poet called T.S.Eliot actually said the fog was like a yellow cat! I suppose they do have the same softness and stealthiness.

But you, Gypsy, bring your blood from the sun of Africa. At least, you've always told me that:

"I'm as black as a Nubian princess, me... Once an Ethiopian sculptor carved me out of a block of pure ebony, and set a disc of gold (the sun) in one corner... Those intimations come to me in dreams, G. It was long before your misty northern Celtic time"...

So I expect you're sitting on the doorstep of Noltland in Deerness today, laved in sunlight. And saying to the encroaching sea-haar,

"Keep your distance, indistinctness and obfuscation, you breath of boreal ice. Remember, you are

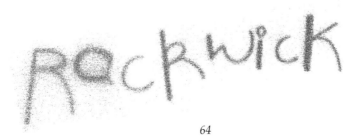

trying to enmesh one who might well have been a princess among the blazing suns of the south. Come too close, fog, and I'll simply walk inside and write a letter to Nora in Edinburgh."

That's what I imagine you **might** be thinking. I could be wrong. Maybe you're a sister of the mysterious fog, after all.

Maybe see you next week.

Long-Ago

Dear Gyps,

Listen to a very sad story.

There was once a lovely little black kitten – I forget its name.

This happened a long long time ago, when your friend G wasn't that old; in fact he was still a schoolboy.

Well, G was fond of playing golf in those days.

This tragic event happened in the back garden of a house at Well Park, Stromness.

It was summer and holiday time.

Kitten

Well, this G was practising "swings" with a golf club, over and over again, in the sunshine.

Didn't this sweet little cat rush playfully at the club as the club was cutting an arc at high-speed, and that – alas – was the end of its beautiful young life. Mortally wounded it lay betwixt the greensward and the sun.

Oh, it was sad!

A neighbour lady let out a series of wails like a masker from a Greek chorus – and my own heart was laden with woe though I didn't utter any lamentation. (Schoolboys don't cry.)

Then my friend Kenny MacInnes and I had to perform a funeral for this little innocent.

A whole golden summer day was brought down in ruins…

I'm glad there are no golf clubs in Deerness, Gypsy. Anyway, you're too wise to do such a thing, aren't you?

But do keep a weather eye open for cars!

Dear Gyps,

Guess what – I've just had 2 dogs in my house, from Cliff Cottage, Rackwick: Glen Hutchison and his new sister, Lady.

Well, as you know, I think dogs are vastly inferior to cats, in looks and intelligence, but Glen is a nice friendly collie, as dogs go.

Says David Hutchison, "I thought Glen would be lonely, so I got Lady to keep him company."

(*As if Glen would be lonely, with all those sea-*

by 2 HOY DOGS

birds, seals, sheep, cows, rabbits – he is even nice
to that most questionable of species, the so-called
"homo sapiens"; as we know who've studied
Latin deeply, "sapiens" means wise – where I
wonder do they keep their wisdom?)

Well, this newcomer Lady is half-collie, half
Jack Russell and she's anything but a lady, the
way she tried to chew Glen's ear off in my house
and snarled and snorted and leapt all round him.

I think Glen must have been a saint once, for
he withstood all Lady's assaults and never com-
plained once. In fact, Glen seemed to be saying,
*"What a delightful bundle of energy this Lady is!
Won't Lady liven up the winter for me and
Hutch? That's my ear you are trying to chew off,
Lady – that's what I hear with..."*

So, if you smell a double doggy smell in Mayburn, Gypsy, you'll know where it comes from…
No, treble doggy: Nuff MacPhail was here the
day before.

waiting

Dear Gyps,

I hear Nora has taken a fancy to a little silvery gray cat in Rendall.

I think she might even like to have it... Well, only perhaps.

Gypsy, if I was you, I would put down my paw very firmly.

"No Rendall cat is going to share a house with me!"... "I'll take to the roads like a tramp if you do such a thing to me."... "At my time of life, all I want is peace and time for meditation and studying the life-cycle of sea-birds"...

Quite right, Gypsy. Just tell Nora that, in no uncertain terms. And you can tell her too, that G will not be responsible for 2 cats in Mayburn Court, ever... You're welcome, Gypsy, when she has to go away, for a week or two. You know that. But I wouldn't entertain another cat along with yourself. Never. Not for any reason whatsoever. Nothing doing. It's not on.

Also, Gyps, I don't want to worry you, but if

fOR Primavera

Nora comes home some day and begins to study you thoroughly, measuring your tongue and the length of your ears and whiskers, and counts your beautiful teeth and puts a card with letters on the wall in order to test your eyes, and peers down your magnificent throat with a micro-scope, and holds you upside-down by the tail for some purpose or other

　　–YOU ARE NOT TO WORRY–
she is just studying Biology.
If N. tries anything like that, just say,
"No thanks, my biology is in perfect working order (if it gets a bit of liver and fish occasionally)... Try your experiments on Bianca or the O'Briens' cat"...

Dear Gyps,

There was once a cat who was offered a bag of gold coins or a bag of pennies: one or the other...

*"Oh,' said this cat, 'I don't know anything about that yellow stuff, but I can buy this and that with pennies. So I'll have **that,** if it's all the same to you"...*

Wouldn't you say that was a stupid creature?

Well, then, a plate of salmon – rarest and richest of fish, after sturgeon maybe – was set before you the other day. And didn't you turn up your nose at it? No, you'd rather have rabbit out of a tin – rabbits! There are tens of thousands of them running wild all over Orkney!

Well, Gyps, it may just be that you're a very democratic pussy, and don't want to flaunt your fine delicate tastes in front of people.

"What's good enough for the farm cats is OK for me"... "Only snobs eat salmon"... "Do the

Thoughts

pussy-cats in the Sudan get salmon to eat?"...
"So just put a spoonful of Whiskas rabbit in my
plate"...

Deep thoughts Gypsy has, sitting in her rocker
by the fire.

King of the

Dear Gyps,

Do you know this, I haven't seen one single pussy-cat in the whole huge city of Aberdeen.

I wonder, have cats been banned from this city?

They must have been. What have they done? What cruel outlandish crimes have they committed?

It all began with the Pictish wild-cat Groll, a long, long time ago, before King Kenneth McAlpine.

Groll walked about under Benachie in the moonlight.

"Cats," he cried, "can't you smell fish? Are your olfactory senses so thick that you can't smell the most delectable sea odours stealing up here on the wind from the region between Dee and Don?"

So the Grampian cats stuck their heads out of caves and corries and their senses were ravished with smells of cod, herring and ling.

Forrester Hill

Groll said, *"They've set up a fishing village down there, between the two rivers. We're in clover from now on. Now, my plan is this, when the fishermen and their wives are all asleep…"*

So, next night when the fisherfolk weary of travail with oars and nets were sunk deep in slumber, Groll and the wild-cats made a foray among the baskets of fish.

The Aberdonians – Aberdeen was the name of that village – weren't exactly fools, and they had a wolf-hound chained to a post, and this monster of a dog set up a howling when he saw the circle of cats closing in. And the fisherfolk ran out with sticks and tongs, and the cats all fled among the Grampians.

No fun, facing a wolf-hound with teeth like a row of knives!

Next week I'll tell you how Groll outwitted the wolf-hound.

Cat Earing

Dear Gyps,

Would you like to hear more about Groll the Grampian wild-cat and Fang the wolfhound that guarded the fish at Aberdeen village, long, long ago?

Groll – what a rash cat! – crept into the village when the fisherfolk were asleep. Fang growled. Groll walked straight up to Fang, who nearly went insane barking and howling. But Groll took care to stay just beyond the length of Fang's chain.

"Fang, my friend," said Groll gently, "I'm surprised at you. Do you mean to say you're happy being a slave on a chain for the fishing people? Shame on you, Fang. You should be a proud independant dog hunting in the mountains, beholden to nobody."

Fang growled and snarled and showed teeth like daggers.

"Next time they come and loosen your chain," said Groll, "seize the opportunity – make a quick dash into the hills, feel the freedom of the wind and clouds, revel in your true inheritance! Don't

forget…"

Groll washed his fight-battered face with utmost delicacy, while Fang raged and howled at the end of his chain.

Next morning a fisher boy unloosed the chain to let Fang have some exercise along the waterfront, and Fang was away among the foothills like the wind – and he was seen no more. (They say a hunter transfixed him with an arrow the next spring.)

"How clever Groll is!" sang all the cats in chorus.

Just how clever Groll was, could be seen next day when the boats unloaded a huge haul of white fish in the village square, and danced around them to a harp and a pipe.

When the fisherfolk of Aberdeen were all in bed, Groll led his brave company of Grampian cats down to the village. They had such a feast till the sun got up! Then they played with the stump of Fang's chain till it chimed and rang. And home to their cave they went, licking their whiskers from time to time…

CAT & BLACKBIRDS

Dear Gyps,

'Hello, blackbird, I know you're there inside, in the barn'-

'No, cat, you're quite mistaken. What you heard was the flutter of a leaf, no more.'

'Understand, this is private property. You're trespassing. You will be evicted, as soon as my mother gets back to Deerness from Stromness.'

'O Gypsy, have pity. Have mercy, sweet pussy! I'm sitting on three eggs, keeping them warm.'

'I don't care what you're doing. You're a vagrant. You're breaking the law. Pay some rent or out you go.'

'O Gypsy, I'm pleading with you. My husband, Jet, and I, must take turns to keep the little unhatched birds warm in the nest. We can't leave now.'

'I'll have to think about it.'

'O yes, think well, Gypsy. Think of the delight-

LIBRETTO FOR

ful kittens you had, how you loved them all.'

'They were beautiful. Some were delicate, some met tragic ends, a few are still flourishing, like William Bevan and George Bewlay in Skye. Motherhood is marvellous, I know.'

'O Gypsy, I can hear their little hearts beating inside the shells. Soon...'

'Oh, tell me how it is with blackbirds.'

'Soon they'll hear mighty cracks and cleavings and crashings like thunder, and the light of May will come pouring in on them from the broken shells and they'll be a bit frightened but even more astonished and glad. And they'll squeak in very tiny voices, 'Food, food.' And their father will fly out, so proud, to look for worms for his new children. Then they'll go hungry again soon, and it'll be my turn to go and hunt worms for those little jewels in the nest.'

'Well, I'll have to speak to Nora about it. You

might still have to pay the Poll Tax for two. We'll see.'

'O good! O wonderful! Nora knows we're here. She was very glad we've come to be her tenants. She's going to see that we're undisturbed. She's happy because of us.'

'Well then, you can stay, I suppose, till the little hungry brats can fly. Then off with the lot of you.'

'Thanks Gypsy, sweet pussy (black and beautiful like us)'…

P.S. I wonder if Sir Peter Maxwell Davies will put this libretto to music, Gyps. We'll have to have a very pure high voice for the blackbird, and a low thrilling contralto for the cat.

Opposite: Cleopatra's First Cat

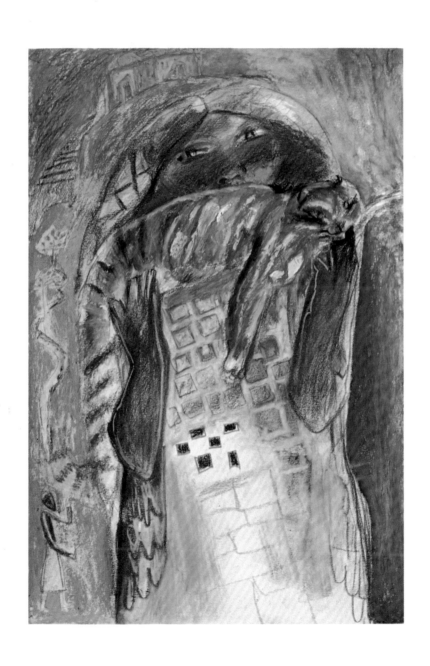

Walk

Dear Gyps

The sun is shining so bright and the air is so calm, I'm sure you must be out strolling as far as the Gloup or the Covenanters' Memorial.

I suppose you'll meet a farmer or a farmer's wife now and then on the way, and raise a paw and say,

"Good morning, a nice day, isn't it…"

And after you've gone past, they'll think to themselves, "What a clever cat that was – it spoke to me…"

Then this person – let's suppose it was a farmer – will go home for dinner, and he'll say to his wife, " A very strange thing, I met a black cat on the road and the cat actually spoke to me"…

The farmer's children will laugh and think their father is going round the bend, or has been at the bottle in the barn (in secret.)

The farmer's wife however will say, "That must have been Gypsy from Noltland you met. Of course she'd have wished you 'Good morn-

in the winter sun

ing.' She's an extraordinarily clever cat. I hope you had the good manners to reply!"

And the farmer will sit ashamed over the soup bowl.

And the farm children will say, "Oh, *Gypsy* – it must have been Gypsy you met, father! Gypsy's different from all the other cats in Orkney"...

Defying the Elements

Dear Gyps,

Thank you for sending me your journal for 1988.
Very interesting reading:

January: *Had New Year with voles and*
blackbirds. Ate one tin whisky-
flavoured turkey. No hangover.

February: *Saw a snowdrop. "Here you are again,*
snowdrop," I said, "Hello." Snowdrop
hung her head, shyly.

March: *Big winds that flattened my ears.*
Steered home through a shouting gale,
steering with my tail.

April: *Deerness is some place, grass and green*
fields, not the hard stones of Stromness.

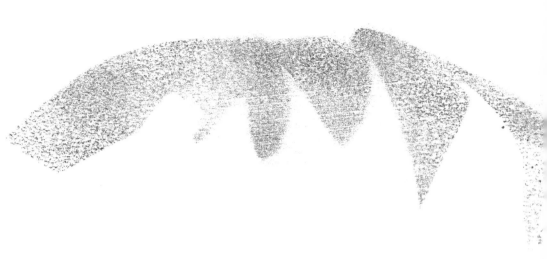

May: *Lot of sun. Don't see the moon, my
sister, much. A pity. Get on well with
cows.*

June: *Post-card from G in Shetland. Lucky
person; he jets all over the world.*

JOURNAL

July: *Glad there's no Shopping Week in Deerness. G. came to see Nora with a French family, the Le Restes. Saw me instead. Sang them a song.*

August: *Went for walks with N. to the beach. Poor seals, all sick – some seal virus.*

September:	*Here's the moon back again. Colder though. Sleep beside N. on nice quilt.*
October:	*N. driving car. Hope I'll get a few nice runs. Sent G a birthday card. Very ancient now he is.*
November:	*I **might** allow my letters to be published. Will get headlines in "Sun" and "People":* **Shocking revelations – Gypsy tells all.**
December:	*"I might stay awake and have a word with Santa" I thought. But of course I was asleep when he climbed down the lum...*

Well, thank you, Gypsy, for letting me read your journal.

A good 1989 to you.

Snowman

Dear Gyps

I heard a rumour that you slept on and on through that sudden snowfall. A thick black huddle on top of the quilt, on and on you slumbered...

And here was I, in Stromness, thinking that you would be out in the garden of Noltland with your spade, clearing the paths and at last building a snowman.

And with the snowman you would have (I thought) a long conversation.

Snowman: *Goodness gracious me, how did I get here! Where did I come from? Amazing!*

Gypsy: *I just made you, the way a sculptor makes a statue.*

Snowman: *Did somebody say something?*

Gypsy: *I spoke, stupid.*

Snowman: *Whatever can you be? You look so thrillingly black against the snow.*

Gypsy: *Now you're here, make the most of it,*

mister. *Because your time is very short. Tomorrow you'll have vanished away.*

Snowman: *I'll make full use of my time. But, you beautiful black sculptress, there are several things you have forgotten.*

Gypsy: *How dare you! I've made you as perfect as can be.*

Snowman: *O no you haven't. Where are the buttons down my front? Where is the pipe in my mouth? Where's the scarf for my neck?*

Gypsy: *Talk about gratitude! I'm going in to sit beside the fire. Here's more snow. Have a good time. Have some snowflakes for your breakfast.*

Christmas-Time Visitor

Dear Gyps,

I hope you were nice to Nora when she came home minus a tooth. I hope you sang her to sleep and stood guard over her suffering gum while she slept, to keep draughts away. See that she doesn't get any snow in her mouth or a star doesn't pierce through her cheek, until the healing process is complete. I know you'll look after her well.

What are you doing these days? Are you sitting in mid-afternoon in the window of Noltland, Deerness, waiting for the first snowflake or the first star?

"Ah, here it comes, night. Now that I've stood guard over the day, and seen the sun to bed, let the shadows gather, shadow by shadow, till they are a thick black clot at midnight. By that time, I, Gypsy, will be sitting beside the fire or lying between Nora's toes and the hot-water bottle, having sweetest dreams of salmon, liver and milk.

"Maybe sometime between sunset and the first star I'll see an old man in a red coat driving four funny horses with trees growing out of their heads. I'll say, 'I see you, Santa, I'm the first pussy in Orkney to see you. Don't forget me on Christmas Eve. I don't suppose you have a new tooth for Nora? No, I suppose not, seeing you have no teeth yourself, Santa, but all the same you're a very kind cheerful old man, and it does my heart good to see you. What's the name of that reindeer with a red nose like a clown? Oh, Rudolf. Hello, Rudolf. You don't need any lamp, Rudolf, to light you to bed. Ha-ha'..."

I expect you think such things.

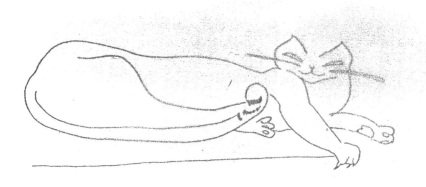

Dear Gyps,

There's a tom-cat very deeply in love in the neighbour's garden. Two nights now he's been singing to his sweetheart, passionately – just when I'm dropping off to sleep.

'Well,' I thought, 'what a *true, intense, ardent* passion must be on him!' Because you see, Gypsy, there was cold snow coming down, and the handsome coat he must have put on to chant immortal poetry to his Juliet must have got all clotted and wet. The snow fell; colder and purer his voice soared up to the balcony where – I'm sure – the loved one must have been lingering; but inside, at her moon mirror, putting the last touches to her hair and her eyes.

'It does no harm to keep them waiting with their bunches of roses and boxes of Black Magic – in fact, it wrings better poetry out of them, purest essence of lyricism, marvellous music they didn't think they were capable of...'

The fickleness of women and cats! She looks

out from her balcony.

'It's snowing!' she says sweetly. *'Fancy that, the snow in late April! Well, surely he doesn't expect me to have words with him tonight. I hope he goes off soon, before neighbours complain. I'll just fill my hot-water bottle and go to bed. Always so good, to sleep in the snow-time'*…

You'd think, Gypsy, the Romeo would go home from the balcony broken-hearted, and vow never, never to fall in love again. You'd think he'd go home and die, either of his broken heart or of pneumonia.

Amor vincit omnia. There he was last night, again, on the garden wall, with a little anthology of new love-songs. This time there was no snow, and the moon was waning. I expect the cruel damsel said to herself,

'O please let him go home, the idiot!… I must have my beauty sleep. There! – I've put out the light and drawn the curtains and barred the door. Go home, you foolish cat! I'll have a sleeping tablet, I think, with my bed-time milk'…

There's women for you Gypsy.

Snow

THE SOLSTICE

Dear Gyps,

You'll never believe this, do you know whom I have sitting beside me on the grass — it is William, your son. William is a little like you, only he's a lot longer and leaner, and he likes to stay out all night.

Just now I was having a cup of tea at Hopedale with Archie Bevan, William's butler and valet, and William actually wanted to drink all the milk out of the jug.

"You selfish creatures," said William, so softly that only the butterflies could have heard him, *"I, William, want a drink too on this hot day..."* So Archie poured milk into a saucer and William drank, standing in the grass.

"That's better," said William. *"It's almost like a picnic."*

Then I scratched William's head between his ears, but he didn't seem to like it as much as you do, Gypsy. I think he isn't quite so sensitive to the tactile subleties that life has to offer...

Still, he's quite a nice cat and you can be proud of him.

Now William has slipped away like a shadow and I don't know where he is. Probably at the kitchen window of Hopedale, asking:

"Can you please bring me a piece of fish... Cheese would do..."

Isn't it lovely, Gyps, all this blue in the sky?

Dear Gyps,

Once there was a cat and this cat got lost. It got lost in April among the long grass and the daffodils.

It was still lost in summer. "Pussy, dear Pussy, come back," cried the kids. One or two of those mischievous kids wept, they missed the cat so much. "There she is," cried one, a dazzle of sun in her eye. But it proved to be a crow in a cornfield.

"I miss that cat!" grumbled an old man as the nights got longer. "She kept my knees warm. She chased the mice that were nibbling my tobacco... Oh, I think I hear her now!"... But it was only the purring of the flames among the peat.

"She was the loveliest cat that ever was!" cried Annabel the cow. "Nobody licked my milk from a bowl the way that cat did. Now here I am, closed up all the dark winter alone in this byre."

One day the snow came in silver whirls and squalls and swoonings. When the world was all

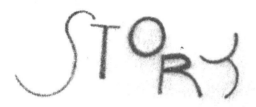

STORY

white, the kids saw a moving delicately dancing black dot on a hill.

"It's only a blackbird!" cried a stupid boy.

But when they came to the hill it was the lost cat.

"So here you are at last," said pussy. *"It's about time. Take me home at once."*

So the cat went back to the croft. Everyone was happy to see her again.

This is just a little snow story to make you sleepy, Gypsy.

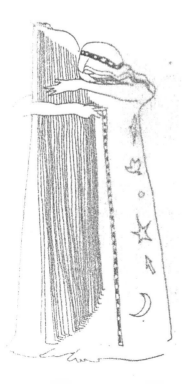

Dear Gyps,

If only you'd gone to the Deerness Agricultural
Show...

The judges would have said, going around
making notes in their notebooks,

"Yes, the cows are especially lovely this year,
so plump and milkful and silky."
and

"Never have we seen such thick-fleeced,
bonny sheep"
and

"Just look at the beards and horns on those
billy-goats – they should be leaping from ledge to
ledge on some mountain-range"
and

"Those ducks and chickens, they ought to be
classed with peacocks and birds of paradise"
and

"Oh, the horses! Such splendid heraldic creatures will still be here when the tractors are
heaps of rust."

Agricultural

At last the judges would pause, in utter won-
derment, and write in their books in capital letters:
THE SUPREME CHAMPION of the SHOW is

GYPSY

the *CAT*...

Then the loudspeaker would announce it and
all the the crowd in the show-park would cheer,
over and over,
"Gypsy!.. Gypsy!"
They'd throw roses over you.
Then you'd walk up and receive the silver cup.

show

Midsummer

Dear Gyps,

I wonder how you like living with Anne Grif-fiths?

Is she good to you? Does she take you to the Hamnavoe for super-duper slap-up fricassees of liver, lamb, and sauces of double cream?

I can picture you, at the Festival weekend, sitting among the famous violinists, actresses, and singers, saying,

"Excuse me, Mr Previn, your bow-tie's not quite straight... That's better... I thought I'd just mention it..."

Then, *"Catriona, I wonder if you have a nice chair with a cushion where I could curl up for forty winks? That's very thoughtful of you"...*

Wanderer

Then, *"Yes, I'm afraid Nora's left me again. Gone to Kirkwall, then on to a place called St Margaret's Hope... Did you ever?"*

"I hardly see G these days, he has so many visitors. No time to spare – not him – for a pussy that was so good to him... That's life..."

Well Gyps, you just stay indoors on June 21 – 22. Because the trows are out those 2 nights. If they saw a black pussy at midnight, sitting on a pier under the moon, that pussy would not be seen, ever again.

That pussy would be taken underground – and live for 100 years among ugly mis-shapen bad-tempered trows.

So watch it.

Defying

Dear Gyps,

Did you ever experience cold like this! In spring too!

I hear you don't want to go outside.

But listen: if you don't go outside to brave the snow and gales, you will grow into a soft vague, fire-fed old pussy. And then, even when daisies and buttercups come, you'll be saying:

"Oh no, the grass has dew on it, disagreeable wet stuff, I might get pneumonia or pleurisy if I go over the doorstep.." So you'll sit closer and closer to the fire. And in June you'll say, *"No, I will not go out – the sun at this time of year can be so treacherous, if a cloud comes and covers it, cold shadows can get into a cat, and there won't even be a fire inside because Nora says it's summer ("no need for a fire") and then I'll begin to sneeze and cough, and my nose will*

the Elements

run..."

That's no way to reason, Gypsy. You have to take little sips of winter, so you can get through blizzards. You must hold up your flower-like face to a few raindrops so that you can stand and defy the thunder showers. (Are you listening?) You must venture into a small cold wind, so you can laugh at gales and tempests, like a wild Siberian cat.

"Oh dear," I can hear you, *"there's G. sermonising me again. Did he ever get to the North Pole? Nobody likes fires and quilts more than G..."It*

Dear Gyps,

What a nice letter from you to me, that Nora brought yesterday. I wonder if she had a glance at it on the sly.

Gypsy, if this horrid, cold mist-bringing East wind goes on much longer, I shall be very angry.

"Oh," cries the wind, *"I love to blow from the east, I'm like the ram-horns of Genghis Khan sounding – I'm like the shouting Celtic tribes, wave after wave, all war-cries! Oh, I could blow for ever!"*

East Wind

That foolish wind, little does it know that it curdles the marrow in the bones of man and cat and makes us quite ill... Especially delicate creatures like you and me...

Whereas, when it blows from the west – which is, after all, the airt it loves best – it brings music and magic to us, seal songs and the breath of mermaids and the merry splurge and dance of whales. And more, it brings aromas of the magic isle in the west that people have known was there for thousands of years. The Gaelic-speakers called it Tir-nan-Og (which means "the land of the young"). Once we're there, believe me, Gypsy, we'll never be old and sick and weary – for pussies there'll be a silver fish on a plate every day, and a nice stone – emerald or lapis lazuli – to sit on always in the sun, and *no dogs* and *no bad-tempered householders* who 'shoo' pussies off their doorsteps.

There, in Tir-nan-Og, even the east wind is gentle and full of scents and sweet sounds. But you have to be *good* to get there.

Dear Gyps,

What a brave pussy-cat.

First day in Stromness, now Nora's off again, and not one step over the door, in case a wolf or a bear was waiting..

Next morning:

"I think I remember this place. I'll take a step or two along the balcony. G, don't you dare shut the door!"

The morning after:

"Of course I remember Mayburn. I often used to come for holidays here. I'll just stretch my legs below, and sniff at the garage doors. G, you don't need to wait. I can find my way back – I'm not exactly feeble-minded"…

Third morning:

"There's the sun shining! I've had enough of rocking chairs and stairs and bedroom. Time to explore old haunts – Margaret's garden, maybe, or Flaws's pier."

(You were gone for half-an-hour, you most

EXPLORER

adventurous cat.)

But we're not always so brave, are we, Gypsy?

There was one morning you were out preening on the balcony, but not for long, because you came bounding in, bright eyed and breathless. What on earth could be the matter? I heard heavy feet approaching, and a letter came fluttering in through the letterbox. Fancy: Gypsy, the great explorer, being scared of the postman!

Well, you haven't had your outing today, have you Gypsy? Promise, if I open the door, that you won't wander off to the big Pier, or the beach at Warbeth, or back to Deerness just to make sure everything's OK there...

"Oh, I might just dawdle as far as the old place in Dundas Street, to have a word with Bianca Wilson and the gulls"...

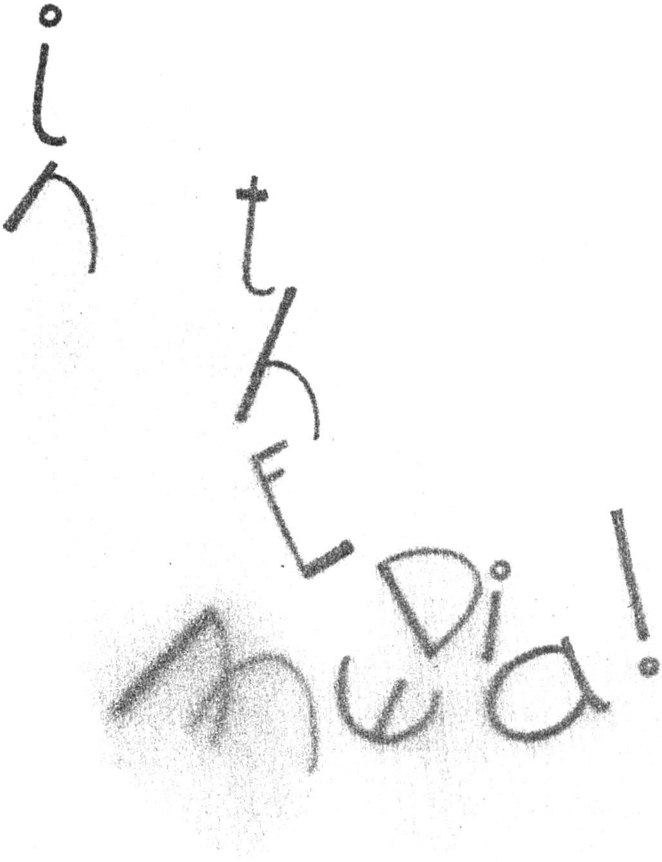

Opposite: A Song at Midnight

Dear Gyps,

I am sitting dazed after 5 days of Festival – dancers and fiddlers, singers and reciters, and exhibitions. Such crowds!

Lucky Gypsy, in the rural peace of Deerness. I can see the way your mind is working – *"I think"* thinks Gypsy, *"we'll have a Feline Festival soon... Something like MacAvity's 'Grand Chorus for 12 Manx Cats and 5 Persian Cats and 50 Abyssinian Cats, with an Eskimo Cat rattling ice-cubes' – what a marvellous sound, eh?"* Then Gypsy warms to the idea –

"I know many good cat singers. Outside, at night, under the moon – fantastic!" And on she enthuses – "Cat dancers too: no human ballet star has the lovely rhythm and balance and poise of us cats"… Then, pondering a little, "There might be a little difficulty with art – But why should there be? If gorillas can paint pictures, what's to stop cats? Imagine, our delicacy of line and gentle pastel shades. Think of our still-lifes of fish and milk bowls. The marvellous paw patterns in dust or in mud… I'm sure there could be a marvellous school of cat artists!"…

Well, Gypsy, you go on thinking about it. You might be onto something big. Festival Director: Gypsy. All the cat lovers of the world would come flocking…

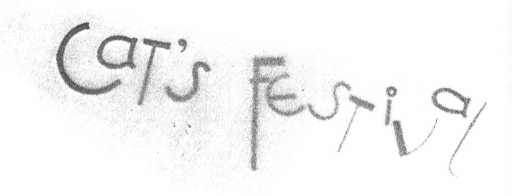

Night

Dear Gyps,

If you only heard the pussycats singing and playing their midnight fiddles around Mayburn Court, you'd prick up ears and be in the window in a flash, looking about everywhere with your brilliant orbs for those talented feline musicians who must be thinking they're sending us off into gentle sleep with their serenades; whereas I wouldn't in the least be surprised to hear the crash of a flower-pot or two on the flagstones, hurled by an insomniac Mayburn householder at the dark song-brimming shadows below, along with offensive remarks (shouted!) about the whole tribe of cats in general.

Music

But I'm told they're only cat-Romeos singing love-songs to their cat-Juliets. And since cats can't send bunches of roses or boxes of rarest perfume tied with silk ribbons, or boxes of Black Magic, that's all they can do to show their love: sing under the stars.

So, Gyps, I'm glad you have a low thrilling velvet voice; because the Deerness farmers won't fire off shotguns at you under the moon, or call you names that no-one should ever call a lady like you.

Good sleep and dreams and purrs to you.

Snowdrops

Dear Gyps

I was at Hopedale yesterday having lunch of kedgeree and dandelion wine.

Where was William? William was not there. Wiliam is sleeping under a bush in the back garden, along with Tyger, Panther and Fankle.

Oh, he is a miss.

But it doesn't do to mourn too much, for the chain of life goes on – not a heavy clanking chain such as criminals wear, but a mysterious chain that binds all the elements together, in joy and harmony.

So, when I was leaving Hopedale for home, Elizabeth Bevan showed me a scattering of snowdrops under the tree in the front garden, risen so sweetly and shyly from winter graves. And she gave me one to take home.

How did you get on in those westerly gales, Gypsy?

Ho, the floodtide came ramping into Stromness harbour yesterday, and covered some of Tam MacPhail's pier. I'm sure that old Dundas St. pier of yours would have had a good drink of salt, and maybe a sip or two for the house too.

I wonder, is Stromness sinking like Venice?

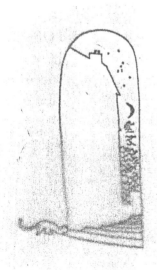

A BOOK

Dear Gyps,

Would you believe this?

A man called Maurice Lindsay, a well-known Glasgow poet, wrote to me asking me to contribute a poem to an anthology about *dogs!*

DOGS!!

Me, write a poem about a dog... It would be laughable if it wasn't so outrageous.

Oh, the tip of my pen was red-hot as I dashed off a reply to Mr M. Lindsay. "Not on your nelly, duff," or words to that effect.

What I told the anthologist of those brutes was that a tiny boy, aged 7, was savaged by a tawny mongrel on the street in Stromness, long long ago. That little sweet happy smiling merry little fellow had to be dragged howling along to the chemist, his knee streaming blood, for the tooth-prints of the brute to be disinfected. And the iodine – or whatever it was – was more painful than the bite. Oh, how the little angel howled and yelled.

about DoGS!

So, Mr Lindsay, no dog contribution from GMB, (for your friend G was the dear little cruelly-treated chap.)

Then I remembered I'd written a poem about a wolf and I sent that instead. I think he's going to use it.

Dear Gyps,

Good for you: gone for a little stroll this fine morning: 2 little strolls. Never been known before, the like of that...

Well, not far.

"I'm not exactly a marathon walker" says Gypsy. *"No John o'Groats to Land's End for this pussy. I sit for a while on Mrs Spence's doorstep next door. I take a turn to see what Mr Yorston's up to, working on his car. Mr Y. won't leave that car alone, always tinkering and oiling. I think there must be something seriously wrong with Mr Y's car"...*

But it's just that Mr Y likes cars a lot.

On rainy days you never leave the house.

"I have 5 or 6 places in Mayburn where I sleep. I like a lot to watch the dogs and people and pussies down below, sitting on the window sill"...

Gyps, you would make good watch-dog. So

alert, up onto the arm of the couch leaping, eyes ablaze, whenever somebody calls.

"Right enough, I'll see to things all right, there are some very expensive books and manuscripts in this house to guard. The visitors look at me and they know at once they must behave themselves in G's house... I'm not a watch-dog, don't insult me, I'm a **watch-cat...**

Gyps, I give up.

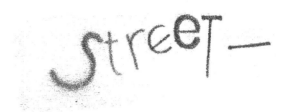

Dear Gyps,

I met a fine handsome cat in Dundas Street,
Stromness.
 "Hello," says he.
 "Hello," says I.
 *"Didn't you once know a cat called Gypsy that
lived around here?"* says he, stroking his
whiskers with a flourish.
 "I did," says I.
 "A pity about her," says he. *"I liked her quite a
lot."*
 "She was popular," I agreed.
 "Got run over," says he. *"A big lorry. They
shouldn't be allowed."*
 "No, she didn't," says I.

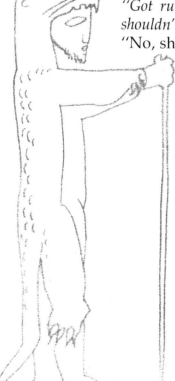

"In that case," says he, *"I must be mixing her up with some other cat. Did she run away, then, with that ruffian of a cat called Heathcliff? She was gone on him, I don't know why. He was good-looking, I admit... Ah well, she'll be having a rough time with Heathcliff. A shame."*

"It wasn't like that," said I.

"Oh, I know," says he, *"one of them tourists just lifted her up and took her on to the 'Ola' with him. Read all about it in the paper. Could be anywhere now, Gypsy."*

"Not at all," says I. "You've got it all wrong, mister Cat."

He thought himself a big cheese, that cat. He fairly fancied himself. A real know-all. Impudent, too.

I was in a hurry to get on with shopping.

"Then," he demanded, obstructing my way, *"what did happen to Gypsy?"*

I had had enough of him.

"Mind your own business," says I.

Wasn't I right, Gypsy?

Dear Gyps,

I don't suppose you'll recognize me next time you see me. But if you see a man with two goldfish bowls over his eyes, that might be me. Because I have my new glasses. If I'd kept on the way I was going, you'd have seen me with a white stick and a guide dog and a begging bowl. Or perhaps I might have stood with dark glasses outside pub doors at closing time, singing for pennies. And then one day when you and Nora were walking near the Quoyberry Inn, in Tankerness, you'd have heard this person singing:

Play to me, Gypsy,
The moon's high above.
Play me your serenade,
The song I love.

Play to me, Gypsy
And when you are gone,
Your song will be haunting me
And lingering on...

NEW SIGHT

Then you'll stop and say,

"I know that voice! I remember it well, from my Stromness period. It's poor G. Look in your purse for a ten-pence piece and put it in G's box"..

But it isn't going to happen that way at all. With my 2 pairs of glasses I can see better than I've seen for forty years

('Forty years!' I can hear you saying, 'what a long age! What a very old man G must be – almost as old as the Old Man of Hoy! – I never realized'…)

Anyway, Gypsy, next time I'll see every single hair in your fur and I'll notice if you've washed your face properly and I'll read from your eyes all the little tricks, thefts, and dodges you're scheming in that little brain of yours. So there.

Nice to see the sun after those four keening hags of days, one after the other. In April, too.

Hallowe'en

Dear Gyps,

Four nights and it'll be Hallowe'en. Imagine the Stromness witch, Bessie Millie*, flying across the moon on her broomstick, with her black cat on her shoulder; Bessie cackling wierdly in the October winds, the black cat rigid with fun and fright − she would rather have been sitting beside the fire, playing games with a mouse, than up there among the streaming stars. Oh yes, she would infinitely have preferred that, Bessie M's cat, holding out her bright paw to a bright-eyed, mouse-hole peeping, whisker-whisking, cheese-smelling mouse, beside the last fire of October.

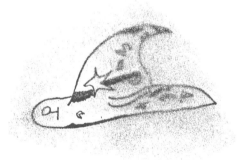

Witches

How pleased that cat would have been when Bessie M. cackled, *'Fasten your seat-belt! Put out your cigarette. Bessie Millie hopes you've enjoyed your flight...'*

Gypsy, don't you go near any old Deerness lady with a conical hat and a broomstick on 31 October. Promise.

* (Bessie Millie – the very old woman visited by Sir Walter Scott in 1814. She sold good winds to skippers sheltering in Hamnavoe for sixpence a time)

Consolation

Dear Gyps,

You must have had such a worrying two days, wondering where Nora was! You paced up and down in your room with knitted brows, conjecturing all things:

*"Has she gone to bring another cat?... In that case, I'll have to arrange for its disappearance – perhaps suggest to it a little walk to the Gloop...
Is she going to move back to that awful stony place, Stromness? – no lovely fields of mice and voles there, only half-mad gulls..."*

No doubt you phoned here and there (the times you phoned me, I must have been out: sorry.)

Well, I'll tell you the truth. Nora was having a mini-holiday in the west, visiting the Pier Arts Centre, weeping with nostalgia at the door of 18 Dundas Street, making stew and eating cakes and drinking coffee. "Boo-hoo" she said, "this would be sheer heaven if only my Gypsy was here"...

in Loneliness

Another lonely cat today, until next Monday, is Billie Ramsey, because her mother is flying to London. When Joanna comes back, what will she find? Tufts and puff-balls and rags of fur everywhere: because that Billie in her rage, grief and frustration lacerates herself in precisely that way.

Also the dog Nuff MacPhail is wandering around Stromness like a disembodied spirit, thinking of ways to get to Gunnie in India.

"Now if I stow away in the 'Ola'… Crossing the Alps won't be easy… Those rabid packs in Turkey too!… And the Himalayas after that."

All you poor bereaved creatures.

Thanks for the lovely snowdrops – they're in a glass in my window.

131

Dear Gyps,

Well, what d'you know?

Here we are on St Andrew's Day – Scotland's national day – and a Scottish pussy like you, descended from a kilted pipe-playing Argyll cat clan ought to be glad about that.

For why?

Because St Andrew was a fisherman and when St Andrew came ashore with his baskets of fish, he had plenty of friends round him, seagulls and cats. Being a saint and a good man, St Andrew would have seen to it that the cats of Galilee got

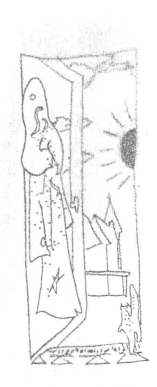

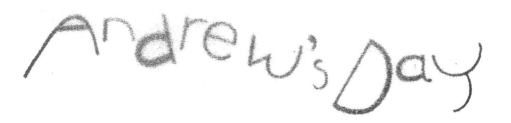

Andrew's Day

nice fish-heads to eat, and he threw them tails and fins glittering from the water.

So, good old St Andrew. And good old Scotland. And long live the ancient, wise, and venerable species *Felix caledonius,* to which you belong, Gypsy.

I don't know if St Andrew ever saw Scotland, or even heard about it. A Galilean fisherman wasn't to know such a place existed. Well, where he is now, he must know about Scotland, mustn't he, because *there* they know everything without having to be told or to turn the pages of books and atlases, and they see all creation and are glad of all creatures: including of course, nice black, bright-eyed cats. Time means nothing there, either; but maybe on 30 November, *his day*, St Andrew looks out from stitching a golden net and claps his hands...

Dear Gyps,

This week when you get your *'Orcadian'*, prepare for a shock.

You'd better have a nice saucer of milk to steady your nerves.

Then get into your comfortable chair, wipe your spectacles, open your paper at 'Under Brinkie's Brae' and your name *Gypsy* will fly off the page and hit you in the eye several times.

Yes, the article is all about your most astonishing behaviour when you were staying here with me in Stromness. When I say "astonishing" I don't mean weird or outrageous or anything like that, I mean astonishing in its beautiful surprising sense.

I hope, Gypsy, you won't reach for the phone and ring your lawyer…

"Yes, I want action taken against Mr George Mackay Brown in Stromness, for publishing a

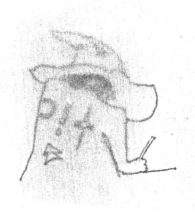

pack of lies about me...Do you have pencil and notebook ready? This is a very serious case of libel, as I hope you'll agree. **'Libel? How libel?'** *Listen, mister lawyer, he says I turfed him out of his rocking chair. Further he says that I ate him out of house and home, He also says I crept upon his umbrella plant at midnight and chewed it up. He says I woke him from sleep every morning with importunate demands for affection, but then he goes on to say it was more food than affection I was after... Surely there's enough there for action to be taken? Surely, for blackening my character like that, I can hound him through court after court, right up to the House of Lords if need be... What's this, you think it's not on – I have no grounds!... I'll say what I think, my man, you don't know your job very well. I intend to consult a lawyer who's read his law books.* **Good-day..."**

Oh, I hope you won't do anything like that, Gyps.

Read it again, and then you'll find the article was written out of deepest affection.